Classic CONCENTRATION

1	2	3	4	5
6	7	8	9	10
11	12	13	14	15
16	17	18	19	20
21	22	23	24	25

THE GAME ★ THE SHOW ★ THE PUZZLES

Steve Ryan

Introduction by Mark Goodson

Sterling Publishing Co., Inc. New York

CIP Data Available

10 9 8 7 6 5 4 3 2

Published by Sterling Publishing Company, Inc.
387 Park Avenue South, New York, N.Y. 10016
Distributed in Canada by Sterling Publishing
% Canadian Manda Group, P.O. Box 920, Station U
Toronto, Ontario, Canada M8Z 5P9
Distributed in Great Britain and Europe by Cassell PLC
Villiers House, 41/47 Strand, London WC2N 5JE, England
Distributed in Australia by Capricorn Ltd.
P.O. Box 665, Lane Cove, NSW 2066
Manufactured in the United States of America

Sterling ISBN 0-8069-8468-6

Contents

Join us on a journey of rebuses and remembrances. That's Bob Clayton, Hugh Downs, and Art James, three great hosts from the original Concentration.

Introduction

There are many kinds of games. Some are designed merely to entertain—to be enjoyed passively the way you'd witness a sporting event from the grandstand. Others challenge viewers to participate actively and to have the fun of competing.

Concentration and its "rebuses" fall into this latter category. Puzzle fans enjoy attempting to solve these visual brainteasers which use a variety of intriguing symbols and pictographs that lead towards phrases, sayings or titles.

Before it became a television show, *Concentration* was at one time a simple children's game. Kids laid part of a deck of cards out on a table face down and attempted to match the positions—an Ace with an Ace, a Queen with a Queen, and so on. The concept of tying the "matching" into rebuses was developed many years ago by Bob Noah, Jack Barry, Dan Enright, and Buddy Piper when *Concentration* first went on the air.

Concentration went through many forms and incarnations on the air. And also through many hosts. The show began originally in 1958 with Hugh Downs as emcee. In its current version on NBC the program is called *Classic Concentration*, and is now under the able guidance of Alex Trebek.

The rebuses we use on the air and the ones in this book come from the fertile mind of Steve Ryan, an inventive and imaginative creator with a flair for puzzles that tease and involve the player.

All of us at Mark Goodson Productions hope that you have a good time solving these.

—MARK GOODSON

STEVE RYAN

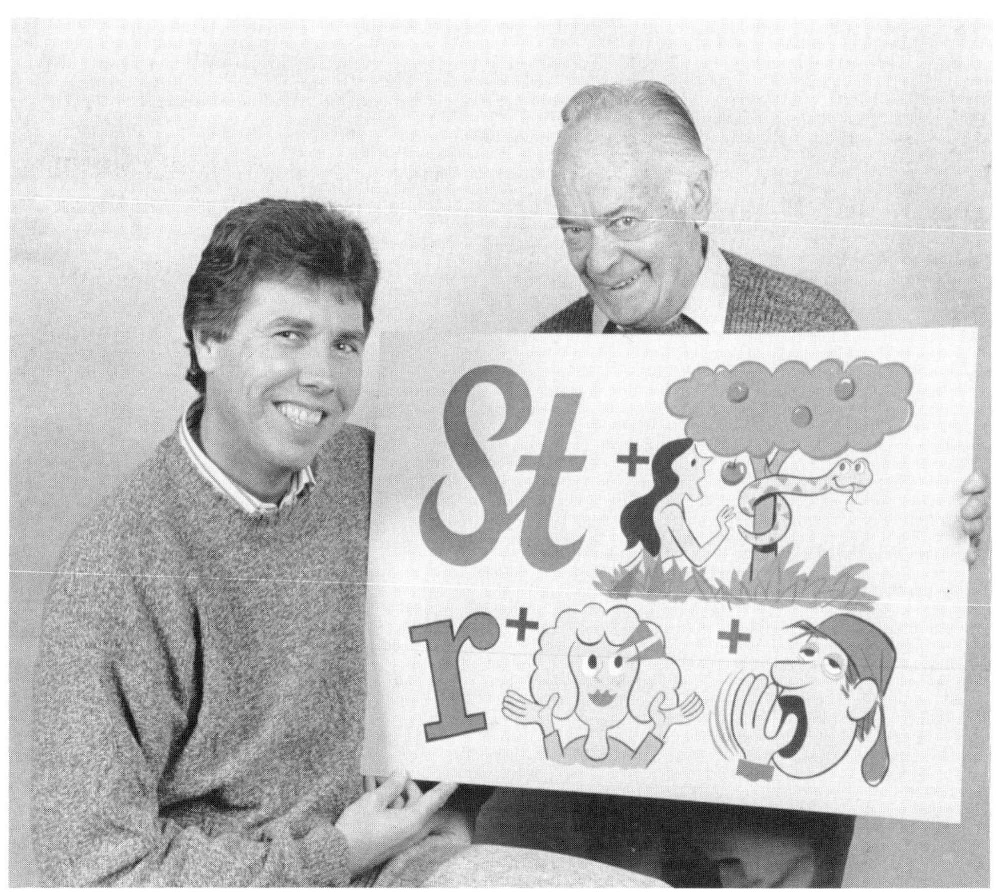

Foreword

"Behind these numbers is a puzzle. Can you solve it?" That's the way we open each *Classic Concentration* show. You may ask yourself, who watches *Concentration*? The answer, millions. *Concentration*'s enduring place in television programming is a testimony to its remarkable audience appeal.

The first portion of this book is devoted to the history of *Concentration*. Gathered here is a collection of memories, trivia and data that will take you on a stroll down memory lane looking at more than thirty years of *Concentration*, highlighted by many "never-before-seen" pictures.

Concentration has the distinction of being NBC's longest-running daytime game show of all time. When *Concentration* first came to the airwaves, it was hailed by critics as the most perfect game ever devised for television. *Concentration* contained all the right ingredients. There was excitement, suspense, viewer participation, and a challenging visual element, the rebus.

And that's what the second part of the book is all about. It's a sampling of my favorite rebuses originally aired on *Classic Concentration*. It's the most exciting collection of puzzles I've ever assembled. There's something for everyone. Some rebuses are pushovers, others are real nail biters; some rebuses are designed to tickle your funny bone, while others are there to challenge the outer limits of your imagination. It all adds up to hours of fun.

Before you begin please read the Acknowledgements and the Long Crawl. These special people, many of whom are personal friends and co-workers, are responsible for *Concentration*'s lasting success and vast popularity. Happy puzzling!

And a *very special* "thanks" to Mark Goodson for helping make this book possible.

—STEVE RYAN
Hollywood, 1991

Above is one of my original sketches. I first visualize the completed rebus in my head and then carefully draw the pictures and letters in the twenty-five grid squares. The final sketch is turned over to the NBC artists, who meticulously recreate the rebus in full color on 20 × 28 inch poster board. Below is the completed rebus and behind it with me talented artist Bernie Schmittke, who painted this puzzle and many others in the book. Bernie has been painting rebuses for Concentration *since the show began in 1958. Other NBC artists include Suzanne Morales, Vern Jorgensen, Carolyn Hughes, and a host of temporary artists. Hats off to them all for a job well done. You guessed it, the rebus says* STEVE RYAN.

One of the very first publicity photos of emcee Hugh Downs promoting his new game show, Concentration. Can you figure out this very easy rebus?

Concentration Memories

Nineteen fifty-eight—what a year it was! That was the year that Ike was in the White House, a pair of blue jeans only cost $3.75, first-class postage went from 3 cents to 4 cents, baseball came to the West Coast, as the Dodgers moved to Los Angeles and the Giants moved to San Francisco, Elvis Presley was inducted into the army, and *What's My Line?* won television's highest award, the Emmy.

It was also in this year that *Doctor Zhivago* was a national best seller, *Gigi* won the Academy Award for best picture, and both *Gunsmoke* and *I've Got A Secret* were among America's favorite shows. How about the year Sweet'n Low, Cocoa Puffs and American Express all made their first appearances?

"The Purple People Eater," "At the Hop," and "Who's Sorry Now?" were all climbing the charts on Dick Clark's *American Bandstand* on ABC-TV.

It was also the year that a young Hugh Downs would emcee his first and only game show—a game show that would flourish throughout the late 1950s, all of the 1960s,

David Schwartz, Steve Ryan, and Fred Wostbrock hold a rebus they used to promote their book The Encyclopedia of TV Game Shows. It reads FORTY YEARS OF GAME SHOWS, *and that's what the book is all about. Now, turn on the applause sign for David and Fred for assisting in putting together this section of "Concentration Memories."*

Emcee *Jack Barry hosted the prime-time version in 1958.*

Hugh Downs, emcee from 1958–1969. Note the plain logo; months later it would be changed to the more familiar one.

and most of the 1970s, then come back stronger than ever in the late 1980s and continue well into the 1990s.

If you guessed *Concentration*, then this book is for you! In this section of the book, we explore the history of one of television's most popular game shows.

Concentration was born in 1958—August 25, 11:30 AM (eastern daylight time) to be exact—and it was an instant hit for its network, NBC. *Concentration* was entertaining, suspenseful, involving, and certainly challenging.

Concentration would become NBC-TV's longest-running game show, spanning more than fourteen and a half years on their daytime schedule. During that period, there were also two prime-time versions, a four-week run in 1958 with Jack Barry as emcee (a quick fill-in when *21* was suddenly cancelled) and a five-month run in 1961

The game board in motion from a 1960 broadcast. The answer is GOING AGAINST THE GRAIN.

with Hugh Downs as host, which was broadcast in "living color." The daytime version was the last NBC show to make the switch to color in November of 1966.

Concentration had the unique distinction of being broadcast from two different locations at the same time. During 1961, the daytime version called NBC Studio 3A in Rockefeller Center home, while the Monday night edition was telecast from the Ziegfeld Theater at 54th Street and Sixth Avenue.

After its fourteen-and-a-half-year run on NBC ended on March 23, 1973 (after some 3,796 shows), *Concentration* returned to the airwaves in September of 1973 hosted by game show veteran Jack Narz. This five-year syndicated run originated from sunny Hollywood, California, rather than from its previous home in New York City. Later, in 1987, *Concentration* returned, but now it was called *Classic Concentration* and hosted by Emmy winner Alex Trebek. Once again, the show was seen on NBC.

Concentration was named after and based upon the children's card game of the same name. The object of the television version was to solve a rebus puzzle by matching pairs of prizes that hid the puzzle.

Two players, in turn, called a pair of numbers (from 1 to 30) which appeared on a three-sided wedge. If the prizes (or information like FORFEIT ONE GIFT or TAKE ONE GIFT) matched, the player was credited with the prize. WILD CARDS were instant matches with whatever else was called. The third part of the wedge was shown when a match was made and revealed two portions of a slowly building rebus puzzle. The player was given a chance to guess the puzzle and if correct, he or she won the game and all prizes credited to him. If not, the player called two more numbers

Host Bob Clayton asks, WHAT'S A REBUS? Simple, it's a puzzle composed of pictures, letters, and words to illustrate a person, place, thing, or phrase.

and tried to make another match. When the pieces did not reveal a match, the opposing player got a chance to call numbers.

The winning player continued to play against new challengers until he was defeated, or until he won 20 games. Only one player, Mrs. Ruth Horowitz, retired as an undefeated champion. She was on the show from July to August of 1966.

The first puzzle used on the original network show was IT HAPPENED ONE NIGHT and the last puzzle was YOU'VE BEEN MORE THAN KIND. Among the regular features introduced during the show's run were "The Cash Wheel" (1960), "The Envelope" (1962), and the annual "Challenge of the Champions" (1963).

During its years on television, *Concentration* has had more than seven different emcees hosting this rebus lovers' game. The first emcee you already know—he was Hugh Downs. Downs hosted the show from August of 1958 until January of 1969. In 1968, he won an Emmy for his hosting duties on the popular show.

Downs was certainly no stranger to television viewers when *Concentration* made its debut in 1958, nor was he a stranger to NBC. First heard on television on such Chicago-originated shows as *Kukla, Fran, and Ollie* and *Hawkins Falls*, he came to New York in 1954 to provide the *Home* show's Arlene Francis with a masculine foil. His outstanding work on this program led to a stint as announcer for *Caesar's Hour* during the 1956–1957 season, at the conclusion of which he joined the Jack Paar *Tonight Show* and years later *The Today Show* with fellow anchor Barbara Walters.

In 1958, Downs, who was certainly a huge success with his "night job" as Jack Paar's announcer/sidekick, was looking for a "day job." A "day job" meant only one thing—either a game, quiz, or panel show.

Gene Rayburn, a game show pioneer himself, was asked to audition for a new game show called *Concentration*. Downs heard about the new show and wanted an

Attack of the coneheads! Actually it's a salute to Scandinavia. That's announcer Bob Clayton at the far left.

audition as well. Downs was given a shot as emcee and it was Downs who won the spot! Rayburn went on to great television fame as emcee of *The Match Game*, one of Goodson-Todman's biggest successes.

During the late 1950s, game shows were hit with scandal. While other shows were being cancelled, *Concentration*, like all Goodson-Todman shows, remained scandal free. At one point in the show, NBC hired a former Scotland Yard detective to give the show added security.

Concentration was such a success on the NBC daytime schedule that a prime-time version was planned for the spring of 1961. *Variety*—an industry newspaper—first said that NBC was planning to use Hal March as emcee. As it turned out the sponsors stayed with Hugh Downs, and he took the emcee podium on *Concentration*'s prime-time bow in 1961.

Hugh Downs was never at a loss for words while hosting *Concentation*, nor was he at a loss for wearing many different outfits from the NBC wardrobe department.

Several times during the year, *Concentration* presented theme shows on which both emcee and announcer would get dressed up in an outfit relating to that theme. Art James, who was the first announcer on the show and would later become an emcee himself, remembers: "Hugh and I loved to dress up in those wild and wacky outfits. We never knew what we'd be dressed up in next. I remember Hugh and I were sailors, Vikings, and monsters at Halloween. . . . Once I was dressed up in a skeleton outfit for our Halloween show and Hugh introduced that day's contestants and I came running out in my realistic skeleton outfit scaring poor Hugh half to death."

Emcees and announcers weren't the only people to wear crazy outfits. Celebrities were fair game too. Each December *Concentration* had its annual Christmas show, for which celebrities dressed up in Santa Claus suits, complete with padding and a fake beard. They played for *Concentration*'s favorite charity, CARE (a nonprofit

Will the real Santa Claus please stand up? Remember the annual Christmas shows which featured guest celebrities disguised as Santa playing for charity?

organization set up to send packages of food and clothing to needy people overseas). At the end of the game, the celebrities took off their caps and beards to reveal who they really were. Children from around the world and in native costumes appeared on stage. After the game, Hugh and both Santas presented them with gifts.

One memorable show, on December 24, 1965, featured the lovely Betty White playing against game show legend Bill Cullen. Cullen was there to promote his upcoming new game show for NBC, *Eye Guess*. Bill was always in high demand to guest and emcee on various shows.

Other guest stars to visit *Concentration* included Burt Reynolds (there to promote his new series, *Riverboat*), the first lady of stand-up comedy Phyllis Diller, *Tonight Show* host Johnny Carson, *Today Show* host Dave Garroway, Joan Rivers, and other television favorites.

Concentration model Paola Diva greets host Hugh Downs with a lei as the show salutes Hawaii on one of its theme games.

While Hugh Downs was no stranger to national television, announcer Art James was. James recalls, "Back in 1958, I heard about a new show that was going to be on NBC called *Concentration*. I was in Detroit at the time at WJR radio and I really wanted to get involved with this new thing called television. So I made an audi-

"Art James reporting for duty, sir!" Art served as announcer for more than two years.

tion tape of myself announcing and mailed it to the show's producers thinking nothing would come of it and in less than two weeks I was announcing *Concentration*!"

So Art James with his family in tow packed his belongings and moved to the Big Apple. James recalls his first day at the studio: "I remember that I was so nervous, here I was freshly plucked from Detroit and planted at NBC for *Concentration*. This was the big time! I was so green that when I spoke into those great classic NBC microphones I actually stopped talking . . . because I heard someone else's voice." James laughs and continues, "What I didn't realize was that the voice I heard was my own, coming over the audience loudspeakers!"

As time went on Art James grew into a wonderful announcer, so good in fact that he was asked to fill in for a vacationing Hugh Downs. James recalls that tape day: "Hugh was going on vacation and the show's producer asked if I would want to fill in for Hugh . . . as the emcee! This was my very first emcee job so naturally I jumped at the chance to be seen on the NBC Television Network. I rehearsed all night wanting to be one hundred percent ready. Things went well, looking back on that memorable event. I do remember a cameraman saying that I was a little nervous. I think he said, if I can remember correctly, that I was 'tight as a drum.'"

Things did go well for the young Art James because in 1961 he left *Concentration* and went on to become a television staple himself, hosting over ten network game shows, beginning with *Say When!*, another Goodson-Todman show, for NBC.

Even though Art went on to host other successful NBC shows, he frequently returned as a guest emcee filling in for Hugh when he was on special assignment for *The Today Show* or on vacation. *(Continued on page 145.)*

That's host Art James pointing to the title of his first network game show. Art made his network debut as an announcer on Concentration in 1958.

The Puzzles

The rebus is a tantalizingly visual puzzle. Its origins date back to ancient Egypt and hieroglyphics. It was this ancient form of picture writing that inspired rebus puzzles. Originally, hieroglyphic writing was a method of restricting specific knowledge to an elite group of people. Only priests and other learned people could read the writings on the walls. Throughout history, there have been many examples of picture writing. In ancient Rome and Greece, there were rebus coins inscribed with pictures that honored famous people or cities. During the Middle Ages, rebuses were used ornamentally on coats of arms, to chronicle a concise pictorial history of a family. Not until the beginning of the seventeenth century did the rebus reach the masses. In France priests distributed religious pamphlets composed of pictures and words. These rebuses became very popular and they served a purpose: now even the illiterate masses could understand a written message.

In America, Benjamin Franklin used rebuses in Poor Richard's Almanac. He created puzzles that conveyed moral messages. In short, these were pictures and words we could live by. What a wonderful way to express a thought. And it worked. The rebus paints a visual image that leaves a lasting impression.

Today, the rebus as we use it on *Classic Concentration* could be called a modern-day hieroglyphic riddle. The big difference is that we use it purely to amuse and entertain. And, anyone can solve our rebuses. We use a visual language of easily recognized pictures combined with letters and words. If you can identify motion lines on an oarsman as "row," the crack of a baseball bat as a "hit," or a sheep with lipstick and false eyelashes as a "ewe," you can solve our rebuses.

The more familiar you become with the commonly used symbols and pictures used to construct the rebuses, the easier the task at hand becomes.

Here are a few tips to remember when solving a rebus. It's not necessary that the pictures relate to the phrase. The only requirement is that the pictures and symbols phonetically convey a pronunciation that is close to the phrase they represent.

A rebus might represent a familiar person, place, thing, phrase, etc.—anything that's currently in vogue. We use plus signs to connect the pictures and letters to create one or more whole words. Flash marks or arrows often highlight a significant part of a picture. If a letter of the alphabet appears with quotation marks, say that letter. It's as easy as A, B, C. If a letter or letters of the alphabet appear without quotation marks, then say them phonetically.

To get you started the first 48 puzzles that follow are presented totally revealed. The next 104 puzzles are first shown with a partial reveal. If you use your powers of observation and maybe a smidgen of ESP, each partially revealed rebus presents a fair chance to be solved. If it's still a little early in the puzzle, not to worry, you can turn the page to reveal the entire rebus. And, if you get stumped, answers to all the rebuses can be found starting at page 155. If you're up to the challenge, and I'm sure you are, welcome to a piece of my puzzling world.

1

Puzzle solutions can be found on pages 155 and 156.

2

3

Puzzle solutions can be found on pages 155 and 156.

4

5

6

7

Puzzle solutions can be found on pages 155 and 156.

8

9

10

11

Puzzle solutions can be found on pages 155 and 156.

12

13

14

15

Puzzle solutions can be found on pages 155 and 156.

16

17

18

19

Puzzle solutions can be found on pages 155 and 156.

20

21

22

23

Puzzle solutions can be found on pages 155 and 156.

24

25

26

27

Puzzle solutions can be found on pages 155 and 156.

28

29

30

31

Puzzle solutions can be found on pages 155 and 156.

32

33

34

35

Puzzle solutions can be found on pages 155 and 156.

36

37

38

39

Puzzle solutions can be found on pages 155 and 156.

40

41

42

43

Puzzle solutions can be found on pages 155 and 156.

44

45

46

47

Puzzle solutions can be found on pages 155 and 156.

48

49

50

49

Puzzle solutions can be found on pages 155 and 156.

50

51

52

51

Puzzle solutions can be found on pages 155 and 156.

52

53

54

53

Puzzle solutions can be found on pages 155 and 156.

54

55

56

55

Puzzle solutions can be found on pages 155 and 156.

56

57

58

57

Puzzle solutions can be found on pages 155 and 156.

58

59

60

59

Puzzle solutions can be found on pages 155 and 156.

60

61

62

61

Puzzle solutions can be found on pages 155 and 156.

62

63

64

63

Puzzle solutions can be found on pages 155 and 156.

64

65

66

65

Puzzle solutions can be found on pages 155 and 156.

66

67

68

67

Puzzle solutions can be found on pages 155 and 156.

68

69

70

69

Puzzle solutions can be found on pages 155 and 156.

70

71

72

71

Puzzle solutions can be found on pages 155 and 156.

72

73

74

73

Puzzle solutions can be found on pages 155 and 156.

74

75

76

75

Puzzle solutions can be found on pages 155 and 156.

76

77

78

77

Puzzle solutions can be found on pages 155 and 156.

78

79

80

79

Puzzle solutions can be found on pages 155 and 156.

80

81

82

81

Puzzle solutions can be found on pages 155 and 156.

82

83

84

83

Puzzle solutions can be found on pages 155 and 156.

84

85

86

85

Puzzle solutions can be found on pages 155 and 156.

86

87

88

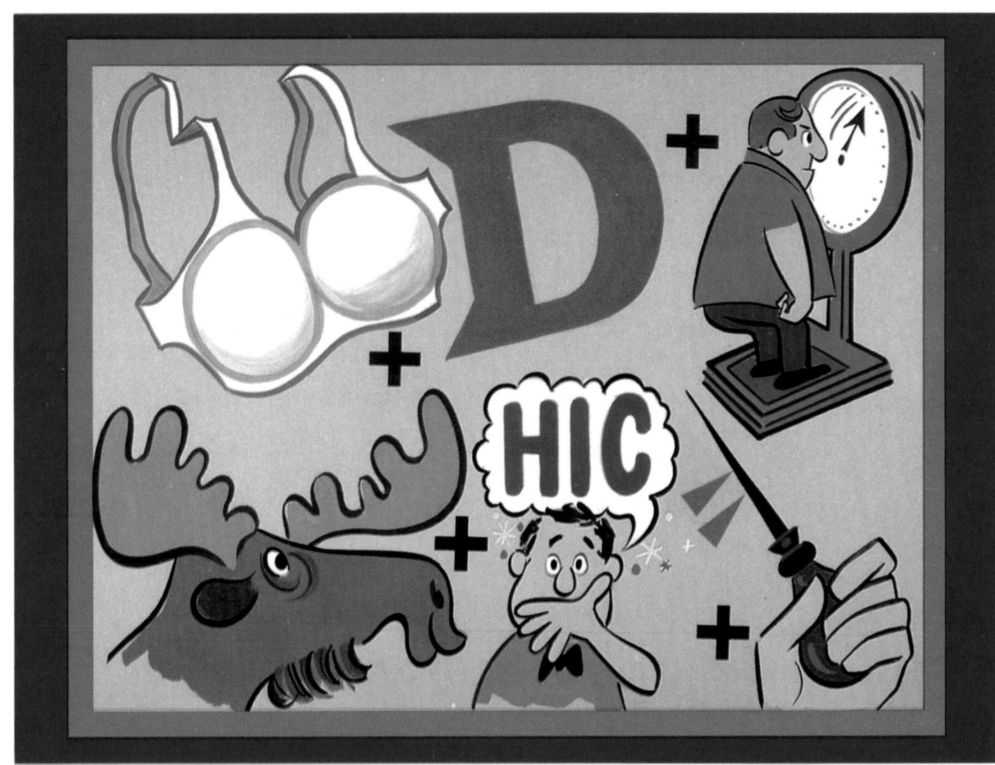

87

Puzzle solutions can be found on pages 155 and 156.

88

89

90

89

Puzzle solutions can be found on pages 155 and 156.

90

91

92

91

Puzzle solutions can be found on pages 155 and 156.

92

93

94

93

Puzzle solutions can be found on pages 155 and 156.

94

95

96

95

Puzzle solutions can be found on pages 155 and 156.

96

97

98

97

Puzzle solutions can be found on pages 155 and 156.

98

99

100

99

Puzzle solutions can be found on pages 155 and 156.

100

101

102

101

Puzzle solutions can be found on pages 155 and 156.

102

103

104

103

Puzzle solutions can be found on pages 155 and 156.

104

105

106

105

Puzzle solutions can be found on pages 155 and 156.

106

107

108

107

Puzzle solutions can be found on pages 155 and 156.

108

109

110

109

Puzzle solutions can be found on pages 155 and 156.

110

111

112

111

Puzzle solutions can be found on pages 155 and 156.

112

113

114

113

Puzzle solutions can be found on pages 155 and 156.

114

115

116

115

Puzzle solutions can be found on pages 155 and 156.

116

117

118

117

Puzzle solutions can be found on pages 155 and 156.

118

119

120

119

Puzzle solutions can be found on pages 155 and 156.

120

121

122

121

Puzzle solutions can be found on pages 155 and 156.

122

123

124

123

Puzzle solutions can be found on pages 155 and 156.

124

125

126

125

Puzzle solutions can be found on pages 155 and 156.

126

127

128

127

Puzzle solutions can be found on pages 155 and 156.

128

129

130

129

Puzzle solutions can be found on pages 155 and 156.

130

131

132

131

Puzzle solutions can be found on pages 155 and 156.

132

133

134

133

Puzzle solutions can be found on pages 155 and 156.

134

135

136

135

Puzzle solutions can be found on pages 155 and 156.

136

137

138

137

Puzzle solutions can be found on pages 155 and 156.

138

139

140

139

Puzzle solutions can be found on pages 155 and 156.

140

141

142

141

Puzzle solutions can be found on pages 155 and 156.

142

143

144

143

Puzzle solutions can be found on pages 155 and 156.

144

145

146

145

Puzzle solutions can be found on pages 155 and 156.

146

147

148

147

Puzzle solutions can be found on pages 155 and 156.

148

149

150

149

Puzzle solutions can be found on pages 155 and 156.

150

151

152

151

Puzzle solutions can be found on pages 155 and 156.

152

Concentration Memories (continued)

When asked if he and Hugh Downs still keep in touch, James responded, "Absolutely. Hugh is such a great friend, and I treasure his friendship. We both had such fun in those early days of television!" When Art James speaks of *Concentration* he remembers it fondly with a smile and a tear in his eye.

Today Art James can be seen on talk shows and infomercials, and you may even recognize his voice on national commercials. Art also heads up Art James Productions in Los Angeles, California, where he stages live game shows for the nation's top Fortune 500 companies. The game shows are designed to teach employees efficiency and productivity. What a wonderful blend of entertainment and education.

When Art James left *Concentration* in 1961, Jim Lucas became the new announcer and remained on the show for two years. Bob Clayton then took over as announcer and the magic clicked between himself and Downs. Clayton remained the show's announcer until he became *Concentration*'s emcee in 1969. Like Downs, James, and Lucas, Bob Clayton would get dressed up in those wild and wacky outfits too.

Throughout its original network run, *Concentration* often dominated its time slot, finishing higher in the ratings than such shows as *Truth or Consequences*, *Play Your Hunch*, *Who Do You Trust?*, and others. The reason was simple: not only did it have a solid format, but *Concentration* was always adding a new element, or so it seemed. Each year they also celebrated both a Christmas show and an anniversary show.

Elementary, my dear Clayton! That's Art James as Sherlock Holmes and host Bob Clayton as Doctor Watson.

Can you remember on *Concentration*'s first anniversary show (August 25, 1959) when Cliff Arquette (better known to millions as Charley Weaver) and Dave Garroway played against each other? How about one year later in 1960 when Hugh Downs played against announcer Art James or in 1963 when Merv Griffin took on Mitch Miller?

Were you watching the day when Phyllis Diller made an appearance on the sixth anniversary show or when Johnny Carson made a surprise visit on the show's eleventh anniversary and played against then emcee Ed McMahon?

Each year, *Concentration* had its annual "Challenge of the Champions," which was started in September of 1963. Each fall the top four game winners in the past year returned to play in a tournament to crown a grand champion. The winner received, in addition to all the prizes, a trip for two around the world and a cool $1,000 in cash. The winner also received a trophy, nicknamed the "Connie," a replica of "The Thinker," a sculpture by Rodin.

Those elements, the anniversary shows, the celebrity appearances, the home viewer games, the theme shows all helped to make *Concentration* a television ratings winner. Oops, I almost forgot about the "$100,000 Shower of Money," where a lucky contestant had 60 seconds to grab as much as $100,000 in five, ten, and twenty dollar bills. Not bad for 1960s television!

Did you mail in your postcard for Bob Clayton to announce your name on television? The first letter of a viewer's last name won a prize behind the corresponding board number.

The annual "Shower of Money," where a player could win up to $100,000. That's announcer Wayne Howell showering the contestant with money.

Hats off to Ed McMahon, who became Concentration's third host. With him is Miss America 1969, Judith Ann Ford. And, heeerrreee's Ed impersonating "The Thinker."

During the summer of 1966, New York television/radio personality Bill Mazer filled in as host of *Concentration* for a few weeks while Downs was on vacation. Mazer's emcee skills were quite good, so much so in fact that NBC gave him his own game show in January of 1967. That show was *Reach for the Stars*. Today Bill Mazer is a top-rated sports anchor and radio broadcaster in New York City.

In 1969, from January until March, announcer Bob Clayton became the newest emcee of *Concentration* after Hugh Downs' departure. Clayton, who hailed from Georgia, was an emcee years prior to his duties on *Concentration*. In 1961 he had hosted a short-lived quizzer titled *Make a Face*. Clayton stepped down from his *Concentration* hosting duties in March of 1969 to make way for new host Ed McMahon, who would continue as Johnny Carson's announcer/sidekick on *The Tonight Show*. Ed McMahon was also no stranger to the role of game show emcee. He had hosted two Goodson-Todman shows in the sixties—*Missing Links* and *Snap Judgment*, both for NBC. McMahon stayed on as host for six months.

In September of 1969, after Ed McMahon left *Concentration*, Bob Clayton became emcee once again. This time his emcee duties lasted from 1969 until 1973. Bob Clayton was a fun-loving person who was very proud to be a part of a show as successful as *Concentration*. Once Clayton became the show's emcee, long-time NBC announcer Wayne Howell took over Clayton's duties as show announcer. As happened years earlier when Hugh Downs was the emcee and Bob Clayton was the announcer, the magic clicked. Clayton and Howell remained a team on *Concentration* until its last episode in the original network run.

Here are Bob Clayton and Hugh Downs reminiscing on the tenth anniversary of <u>Concentration</u>*. The trophy, a replica of "The Thinker," is given to the winner of the annual "Challenge of the Champions."*

During his role as emcee, Clayton made numerous appearances on other top NBC game shows. He was a guest on *Hollywood Squares*, *It Takes Two*, *Jeopardy!*, and *The Who, What or Where Game*. After *Concentration* was cancelled by NBC in 1973, Clayton found great success as an announcer for many game shows. If you tuned into these game shows, it was Bob Clayton's voice that you heard: *Blankety Blanks*, *Pass the Buck*, *Shoot for the Stars*, and *The $10,000 Pyramid*.

Art James recalls a funny Bob Clayton story: "I was across the hall at NBC doing *The Who, What or Where Game* when I smelled smoke coming out of the *Concentration* studio. Moments later I heard Bob's voice yelling for water. It seemed that the rebus board caught fire—nothing serious, just an electrical fire. Poor Bob was the first emcee that I knew who hosted a game show that almost went up in flames!"

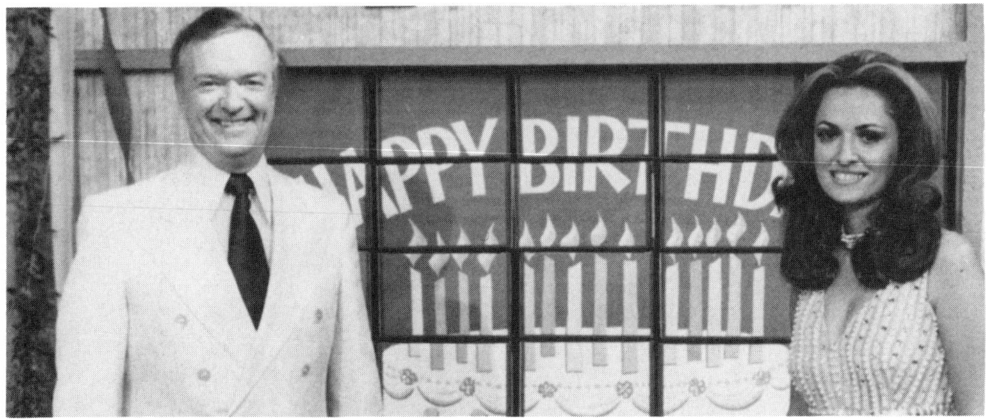

Bob Clayton and model Paola Diva celebrate 14 years of brain-busting rebuses in 1972.

In September of 1973, *Concentration* was back on the airwaves. Game show master Mark Goodson was at the helm of this new version of an old friend. Game show favorite Jack Narz was the show's newest emcee. Joining him was veteran announcer Johnny Olson. We all have fond memories of Johnny. He was the "King of Game Show Announcers," best known for his "Come on down!" line from *The Price Is Right*.

This version of *Concentration* lasted five seasons. Unlike the network run of *Concentration*, this entry had a beautiful new set and a new logo design. The contestants still won those great prizes; now, however, they also had a shot at winning a brand-new car. The car round was called "Double Play" and all they had to do was solve two fully revealed rebuses in ten seconds.

Jack Narz hosted this show with such a smooth, easy style it was a natural that the show would have a successful run. In 1974, during the second season of the revived *Concentration*, Mark Goodson also employed him to emcee his company's newest CBS game show, *Now You See It*. Narz was happily emceeing two different Goodson-Todman shows at the same time. In some cities Narz was even opposite himself.

Jack Narz is quick to point out, "Back in 1974 I sure was tired! I would tape seven *Concentration* shows a day, three times a week usually from Wednesday to Friday, and then on Saturday and Sunday, I'd be doing *Now You See It*. It was hectic but it sure was a lot of fun! . . . Before *Concentration* and *Now You See It* I had an opportunity to guest-host the original *The Price Is Right*, when Bill Cullen went on vacation for a month. Then I emceed the syndicated version of *Beat the Clock* for several seasons." Both of these shows were also Goodson-Todman Productions. Jack Narz had a long career hosting such favorites as *Seven Keys* and *Video Village*.

Wow! Those rebuses from the 1970s were really tough. Jack Narz tries to break it down.

Denise is overjoyed. She has just solved the puzzle and won all the prizes on her side of the board. Emcee Jack Narz and her opponent, Tom, congratulate her.

When asked if he remembered any funny moments from *Concentration* Narz explained, "The set was great; however, that rebus board was still temperamental! It really had a mind of its own! Many times when a contestant called two numbers the rebus blocks would rotate and keep rotating . . . revealing part of the puzzle. This would continue until our director had to yell 'CUT!' " Narz added, "We never had a fire like the NBC network version; however, we did come close a few times!"

Today Narz keeps busy doing commercial voice-overs and playing his second-favorite game, golf.

A happy contestant figured out the rebus. Can you? The answer is PICCADILLY CIRCUS.

For close to nine years *Concentration* lay dormant from the television airwaves.

When *Concentration* came back in 1987, it was bigger and better than ever. Again under the skillful direction of Mark Goodson, *Concentration* had a faster pace and an exciting new look for its re-emergence into the 1990s!

Updated and with its revised format, *Concentration* now became *Classic Concentration*. Taking over as host was Alex Trebek, who had emceed his first American game show in 1973, the same year the original *Concentration* left NBC. Joining Alex on *Classic Concentration* were model Marjorie Goodson Cutt and veteran game show announcer Gene Wood. Once again the magic was all assembled.

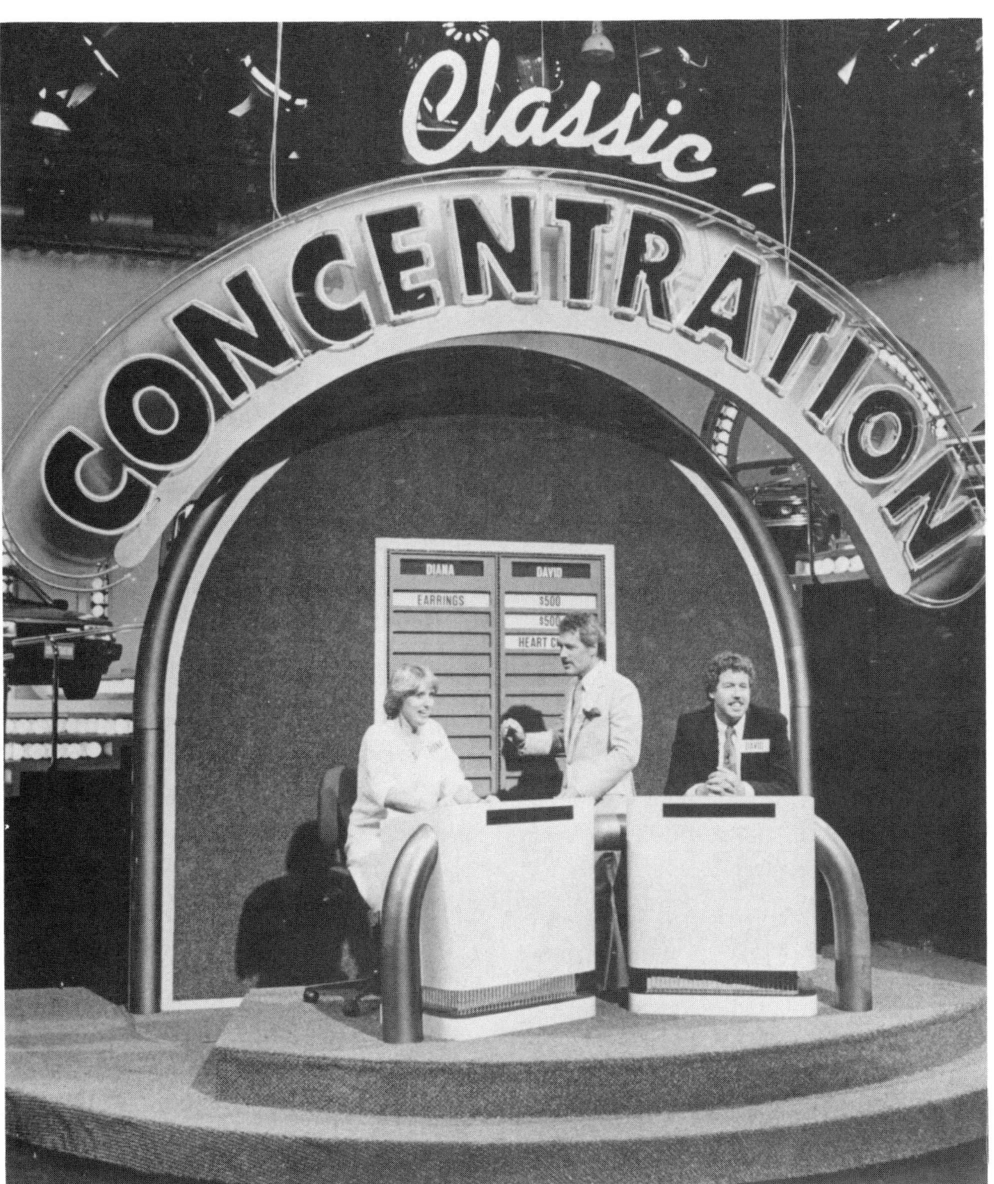

A classic returns! It's now called Classic Concentration and Emmy winner Alex Trebek is its host.

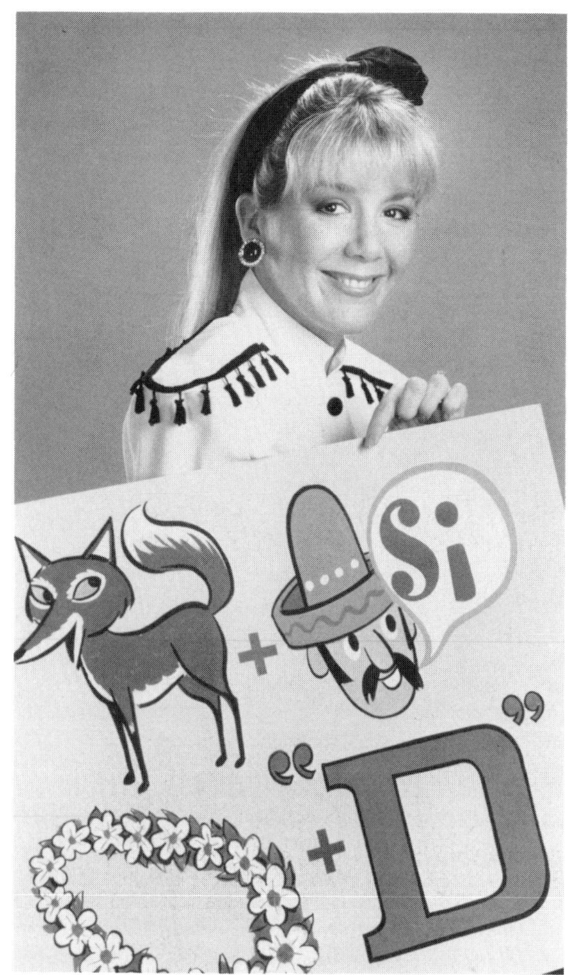

The rebus says it all; that's FOXY LADY *Marjorie Goodson Cutt.*

The set now has a contemporary flair and is extremely innovative. Gone is the old mechanical rebus board of 30 squares; in its place is a new fully computerized game system complete with state-of-the-art color graphics and a 25-square game board designed for faster play.

When *Classic Concentration* returned, some of the rules of the game changed. Originally, when a player lost a game, that was it. Now, all players can continue on the show until they either win a new car or accumulate two losses.

How fast can the puzzle be solved? Would you believe with only two squares exposed and only the top of an apple core showing, a contestant guessed NIGHT COURT and was right! Sometimes a stab in the dark can pay off and as always, there is no penalty for a wrong guess.

Have you ever noticed how the prize cards magically appear on the board behind the contestants? It's still done the same way it was over thirty years ago. The technique is deceivingly simple. The prize cards are positioned behind the blue cards already in place on the board. And, when a match is made, the blue card is pulled and presto, the prize card pops on screen!

One of the new features added to *Classic Concentration* is the "Car Game." After winning the "Puzzle Game," the champ gets a chance to win one of eight new cars that are displayed in the studio. How do they get the eight cars on the platforms that surround the back of the set? That is one of the most frequently asked questions during a taping of *Concentration*. Announcer Gene Wood's favorite reply is, "My wife drives them!" Actually, the cars are driven onto special pallets. The pallets are then hoisted into the air and individual platforms are rolled under them. The staircase of eight platforms is then assembled in place, forming that exciting elevated look.

Using a game board of 15 numbers, a player tries to match seven of the car names that appear behind them. The eighth car name has no match. If a player can make all seven matches in the allotted time, he wins the last car he matched. A player begins with a base time of 35 seconds, and each time he returns to the winner's circle he gets another five seconds added to the base time. How fast can someone play the car game? To date, the best time has been 25 seconds! In the first four years of the show, nearly 350 cars have been given away—that's almost three cars a week!

Classic Concentration has continued the tradition of an annual tournament of champions. Since players don't remain on the show for more than a few days, the players with the fastest times in the "Car Round" return to play for additional prizes and the chance to win another car.

Theme shows also continue to be a part of *Classic Concentration*. In addition to the usual holiday shows, *Concentration* took a week to spotlight the 20th anniversary of Woodstock in the summer of 1989. Even host Alex Trebek let his hair down and put on his love beads.

Every Valentine's Day, Alex picks up his bow and arrow and plays Cupid on "Love Week." That's where couples work as a team to solve rebuses with romantic flavor.

On Halloween shows Alex has been known to dress up as Batman, Zorro, Dick Tracy, Dracula, and other costumed favorites.

Since *Classic Concentration* tapes at NBC in beautiful downtown Burbank, some of Hollywood's brightest stars stop by to see Alex, Marjorie, and little Pokey (more about that cute little rascal in a moment). *Classic Concentration* tapes in studio 3, which is directly across the hall from *The Tonight Show*, home of Johnny Carson and former *Concentration* emcee Ed McMahon. Often, well known celebrities, while waiting to go on *The Tonight Show*, will poke their heads into the studio to see

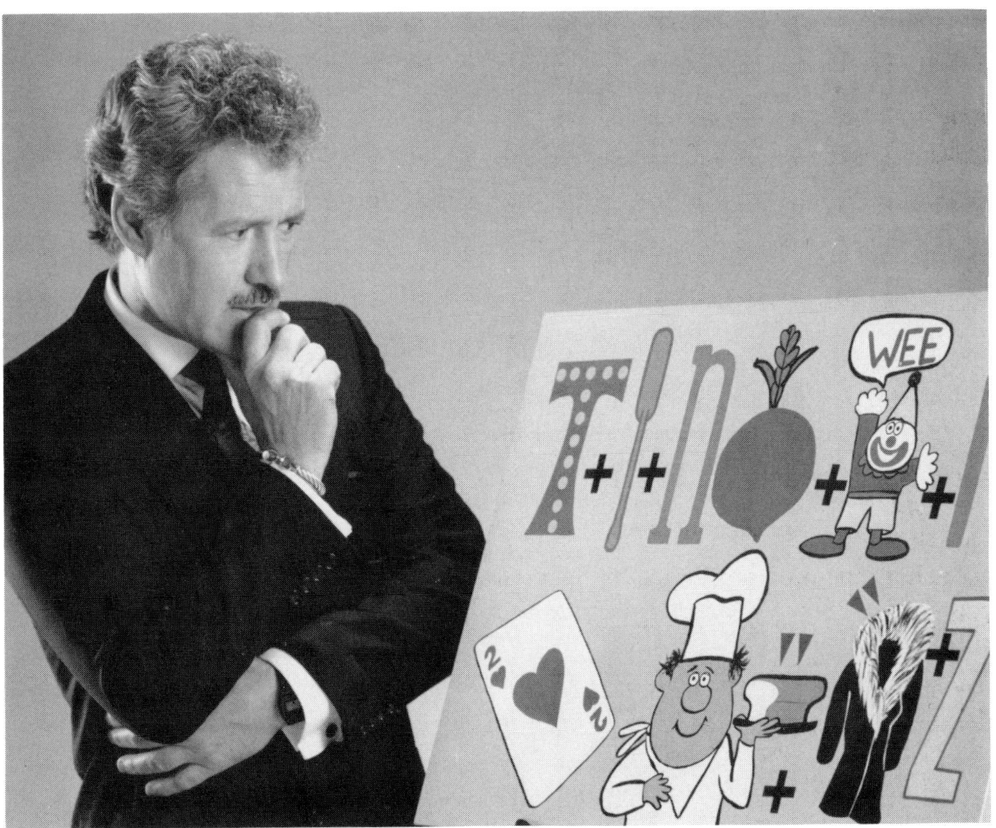

Alex Trebek deep in thought. Can he solve this rebus? It says, TORN BETWEEN TWO LOVERS.

Classic Concentration. Celebrities often do walk-ons and visit with Alex. Were you watching when legendary blues artist B.B. King and top comic Buddy Hackett dropped by?

When Bob Hilton was named the new host of *Let's Make A Deal* he did a walk-on and was presented with a rebus promoting his new show. You guessed it, the rebus read LET'S MAKE A DEAL.

Now let's get to Pokey. Pokey is model Marjorie Goodson Cutt's pet and is often a real scene stealer. Remember when Pokey was seen rocking in a baby's cradle or when Pokey was dressed up as a reindeer complete with antlers? How about when both Marjorie and Pokey were demonstrating a jet ski? And, when Pokey actually played a piano keyboard? He's such a part of *Classic Concentration* that he gets his own fan mail and lots of it! Even matchmakers try to set up Pokey with doggy dates.

The stars of Classic Concentration. That's Alex, Marjorie, and, of course, Pokey.

Birthdays also play an amusing role on *Classic Concentration*. Quite often, special rebuses (the ones that open the show) are created featuring the names of Alex, Marjorie, and show staffers.

Since he was born on July 22, Trebek's lucky number is "22" and it is frequently used by contestants as the first number they call when starting a game.

Classic Concentration has been Alex Trebek's most successful network game show, and now 1991 has brought more good fortune to Alex. In addition to hosting *Classic Concentration* and *Jeopardy!*, Alex has become the new host of *To Tell the Truth*. This puts Alex in a class all by himself.

Classic Concentration may come and go with new hosts and innovations, but it's clear to see that *Concentration* and its rebuses will be around for a long, long time.

The Solutions

Solutions to even-numbered puzzles are found on page 156.

1 Three ring circus
3 Frankenstein
5 Pittsburgh, Pennsylvania
7 Lazy Susan
9 Rock of Ages
11 Columbus, Ohio
13 The pearly gates
15 Count me out
17 Make a new start
19 Bouncing baby boy
21 David Copperfield
23 The Three Musketeers
25 Grandma Moses
27 Georgia peach
29 Chopsticks
31 The Greatest Show on Earth
33 Bill Bailey
35 You were meant for me
37 Idle hands
39 Twenty-twenty vision
41 Inspiration Point
43 Adding insult to injury
45 Where the buffalo roam
47 Mission Impossible
49 You talk too much
51 For richer or poorer
53 A narrow escape
55 That's hard to swallow
57 Roman numeral
59 Crocodile Dundee
61 Twinkle, Twinkle Little Star
63 Confusing the issue
65 Shotgun wedding
67 Dear John letter
69 Don Quixote
71 The tip of the iceberg
73 Your Cheatin' Heart
75 Good time Charlie
77 Stark raving mad
79 Rotten to the core
81 Nowhere to be found
83 No tell motel
85 Johnny Carson
87 Broadway musical
89 Lead pipe cinch
91 Sorry about that
93 Corner the market
95 Denver, Colorado
97 John Q. Public
99 United States
101 Little Brown Jug
103 Blonde bombshell
105 On a silver platter
107 Ride the gravy train
109 Heavens to Betsy
111 Straight from the heart
113 Heaven only knows
115 Taking evasive action
117 Microwave oven
119 Service with a smile
121 Sitting on a powder keg
123 Smart Alec
125 An ounce of prevention
127 Stick to your guns
129 Go for broke
131 A cast of thousands
133 Buckingham Palace
135 Step on the gas
137 Don't cough in my face
139 The sole survivor
141 Three Blind Mice
143 Front row center
145 Onions make your eyes water
147 Phantom of the Opera
149 That ought to teach you a lesson
151 Badgering the witness

The Solutions

Solutions to odd-numbered puzzles are found on page 155.

2 Camelot
4 Polly want a cracker
6 A king's ransom
8 Forget-me-not
10 Blow your top
12 Flying saucer
14 Checkmate
16 Hooray for Hollywood
18 Chief cook and bottle washer
20 Back to school
22 Zip-a-dee-doo-dah
24 Monkey see, monkey do
26 Nutcracker Suite
28 Mad as a hornet
30 Strike it rich
32 Chevy Chase
34 Brand spanking new
36 Bells on bobtail ring
38 Hot as a firecracker
40 A closed mouth catches no flies
42 Billiard table
44 Absent minded professor
46 Wichita, Kansas
48 Be still my heart
50 Jump on the bandwagon
52 Georgia on My Mind
54 Kiss it goodbye
56 Say your prayers
58 Seventy-six Trombones
60 Use your head
62 A harebrained scheme
64 Do not disturb
66 I love a parade
68 Love and Marriage
70 He's a real heartbreaker
72 It's not polite to point
74 Narrow minded
76 Handle with kid gloves
78 Chocolate chips
80 Ghostbusters
82 The Battle of Gettysburg
84 When it rains, it pours
86 A crackpot idea
88 Pepperoni pizza
90 Once in a blue moon
92 The shy, retiring type
94 An iron clad contract
96 You can't change a leopard's spots
98 A change of scenery
100 The Boston Red Sox
102 I now pronounce you man and wife
104 Fourteen carat gold
106 Frankly speaking
108 Anchorage, Alaska
110 MacArthur Park
112 Smoke Gets in Your Eyes
114 Statute of Limitations
116 Laugh all the way to the bank
118 Slippery when wet
120 Read between the lines
122 For all practical purposes
124 Misery loves company
126 Borrow from Peter to pay Paul
128 Working capital
130 Meeting the problem head on
132 Only time will tell
134 Mickey Mouse Club
136 Swallow your pride
138 Napoleon Bonaparte
140 The mark of excellence
142 Strangers in the Night
144 Chicken Chow Mein
146 Spiral staircase
148 Vice versa
150 To Kill a Mockingbird
152 Take it to the limit

Acknowledgements

The author would like to thank the following people and photo services for helping gather information and pictures used in the book.

Mark Goodson, Fred W. Wostbrock, David Schwartz, Jonathan Goodson, Jeremy Shamos, Roy Blakeman, NBC, Brandon Tartikoff, Jackie Smith, Brian Frons, Mike Bevan, Jonathan Littman, Hugh Downs, Art James, Bill Mazer, Ed McMahon, Jack Narz, Alex Trebek, Marjorie Goodson Cutt, Wayne Howell, Gene Wood, Chester Feldman, Howard Felsher, Gabrielle Johnston, Marc Breslow, Ted Cooper, Mark Bowerman, Bernie Schmittke, Bob Davis, Tim Cutt, Jeff Nagler, Chip Lewis, Randy Townsend, Joel Lawrence, Gary Barlow, Bob Boden, Steve Leblang, Willard Tressel, Brian Conn, Dan Cross, Dan Einstein, Liz Martin, Marge Van Ostrand, Stephanie Ryan, Rhoda Sherman, Jerry Leshgold, David Shaw, Brian Brooks, Darryl Regan, Edgar Sotomayor, Hillary Kaplan-Felker, Susan Epstein, Joni Hilton, Bob Hilton, The Cleveland Press, Jim Victory Television, Syracuse University, USC Archives, UCLA Film & Television Archives, William Paterson College, Canter's Deli, and the photo research library from the Howard Frank Archives located in Brooklyn, New York.

It's getting late in the game. Can you solve this rebus? That's right . . . I SHOULD'VE STAYED IN BED.

The Long Crawl

Executive producers
Chester Feldman
Howard Felsher
Producer
Gabrielle Johnston
Directed by
Marc Breslow
Associate producer
Steve Ryan
Creative consultant
Theodore Cooper
Associate
Mark Bowerman
Art directors
James J. Agazzi
Molly Joseph
Martin Bookwalter
Contestant coordinators
Jerry Modine
Maggie Speak
Sharon Yvonne Moses
Beverly Pomerantz
Beverly Morrison
Greg Hughart
Production staff
Kristin Bjorklund
Stuart A. Smith
John C. Melka
John Genung
Phyllis Coblentz
Danny Merritt
Kate Conway
Phyllis Durant
Andrea Moraz
Michael Stephenson
Eric Weyenberg
Cathi Nicholson
Kevin Slusarski
Pam Zimmerman
Donya Braun
Donna Bennett
Ingrid Dresselhuys
Valerie Cook
David Schwartz
Gary Dawson
Heidi Gibson
Sharon Tydell

Prize coordinators
Gail Liddle
Debra Church
Marilyn Andrews
Peggy Parker
Theresa Savage
Gwen Berohn
Joanne McCracken
Monica Barker
Cathy Mauro

Cue cards
Patty Enright
Spencer Enright
Nicki Trebek

Computer graphics
Corey J. Cooper
Kenneth J. Silverstein

Electronic graphics
Jacqueline Frazier
Greg Murphy
Skip Williamson

Electronic still store
Chuck Droege
Beth Lutman

Videotape editors
Bill Paulson
Dick King

Audio
John Macheca
Dave Cone
Wendy Rotoli
Pat Lucatorto
Video
Paul Zigabarra
Steve Kamen
Music
Score Productions, Inc.
Music director
Stanley Blits
Costume supervisor
Alan Mills
Fashion coordinator
Sherrell Paris
Production managers
Bob Davis
Marti Cone
Graphic artists
Bernie Schmittke
Suzanne Morales
Vern Jorgensen
Carolyn Hughes
Associate directors
Tim Cutt
Jeff Nagler
Stage managers
Stuart A. Smith
Alain Delorm
Cathy Hammer
Dan Diana
Technical directors
Vernon P. Lombard, Sr.
Julian Bender
Dick Roeker
Lou Fusari

Lighting directors
Stephen Simpson
Steve Cunningham
Cameras
Jerry Michelsen
Jim Crossman
Ron Lawson
Vince Ybarra
Jim Patrick
Mike Mecartea
Karl Harris
Jim Bragg
Kurt Tonnessen
Ray Liu
Technical manager
Stan Blitz
Manny Montez
Don Talbot
Bob Patchin
Manager staging services
Guy Caruso
Production managers for NBC
Tom Patino
Fran French
Forest Ludwig
Timothy J. Stevens

Distributed by
Victory Television, Inc.

Based on a concept by
Buddy Piper

About the Author

STEVE RYAN

If the world's greatest magician was Harry Houdini, and the world's greatest detective was Sherlock Holmes, then surely the world's greatest puzzle and game master is Steve Ryan, creator of more brain-busting bafflers than anyone in the world.

This virtuoso of vexation has been inventing games and puzzles since childhood. He eventually syndicated his *Puzzles & Posers* and *Zig-Zag* features with Copley News Service and currently appears in more than 150 newspapers across the United States and Canada.

Hoping at first to match the records of world famous puzzlists Sam Loyd and Henry Dudeney, both of whom created 1,500 puzzles in their lifetimes, Ryan has instead surpassed his heroes by inventing more than 10,000 mental temptations that keep puzzle enthusiasts happily climbing the walls. Many expect him to top the 20,000 puzzle mark by the end of the century.

Ryan's creative genius has also catapulted him into television, where he co-created and developed the TV game show *Blockbusters*, for television's most prestigious game show packager, Mark Goodson. Ryan has also written for *Password Plus*, *Trivia Trap*, *Body Language*, and *Catch Phrase*. He currently creates all the rebus puzzles for TV's *Classic Concentration*.

Taking inspiration from the world around him, Ryan's well of ideas never runs dry. As a firefighter for seven years in Southern California, he not only tested his cranium crackers on the crew, but made a puzzle out of nearly everything in the station. Fire hoses found their way into a maze, his "Grass Fire" puzzle stemmed from his work, and other scramblers, math teasers, word games, and mechanical mind-wrenchers evolved from Ryan's analytical view of daily life.

Ryan is the author of such popular books as *Brain Busters*, *Our Puzzlerama*, and *Puzzles, Posers & Pastimes*, and the co-author of *The Encyclopedia of TV Game Shows*, the most comprehensive book of its kind.

Many predicted Ryan's gifts in art, design, and mathematics would lead to architecture. But as usual, Ryan had a surprise twist in store: he built a mental gymnastics empire instead.

Nothing puzzling about that.

Rebus Index